1ST EDITION 2024

MASTERING TINKERCAD
STUDENT

ED CHARLWOOD

PUBLISHED BY

C CADclass

1st Edition April 2024

ISBN-13: 979-8-9881894-2-8 (Student Version)

ISBN-13: 979-8-9881894-3-5 (Instructor Version)

Library of Congress Control Number: ##########

Publisher: CADclass

Written By: Edward Charlwood

Edited: Jake O Sugden & Joshua Manley

For information on distribution, translation, or bulk sales, contact Ed@CADclass.org directly.

About the Authors

Ed Charlwood is an award-winning educator and expert in CAD curricula development, with a Bachelor's degree in Engineering & Product Design and a Master's in Education from Cambridge University.

With 20 years of teaching experience and a passion for empowering students, Ed has crafted STEM curricula for 10,000+ students worldwide.

His approach to teaching has earned him prestigious accolades and recognition, including the honor of being a Google Certified Innovator, an Apple Distinguished Educator, and an Autodesk Academic Partner. He also serves as a Fellow of the Royal Society, which recognizes people who make a "substantial contribution to the improvement of natural knowledge, including mathematics, engineering science, and medical science." He's a member of the Tinkercad Instructor Advisory Board.

Professor Joshua Manley is an entrepreneur and educator with a passion for making. He is a published scientist who ran a science tutoring business in New York City, teaching Math, Chemistry, Biology, Physics, and SAT/ACT prep. He then led the education department of one of the nation's largest and most successful makerspaces. He's taught thousands of students, educators, and administrators worldwide. His TED-Ed talk about bicycle physics has millions of views.

Jake O Sugden is a mechanical engineer and lifelong maker passionate about engineering and design. He taught many making disciplines at one of the nation's premier makerspaces, testing many of the concepts found in this book over the last six years with thousands of students. He is co-owner of CADclass, an CAD education company focused on product development and education. He's an Autodesk expert who works with these programs daily.

How To Use This Book

Welcome to the fantastic world of Tinkercad!

Get ready to mix fun and learning and pick up some amazing new design skills.

This workbook is your trusty sidekick to the tutorials waiting for you at **Tinkercad.com/learn**. So jump in, then come back here to test your skills, push your limits, and take on exciting challenges. Let the adventure begin!

To keep track of your progress, you should check these boxes.

If you see one of these, write your answer in it.

There is a glossary at the back. Write definitions on the dashed lines as you find them out.

When you see this .... write your answer on it.

Pan ..*Changes the view left/right or up/down*

The most important thing is to play, explore, and have fun.

If you'd like to read this on a computer or iPad, visit <u>CADclass.org/pages/books</u> for a free or donation-based copy of this book and others.

What is CAD?

Imagine you're an architect and you want to build an amazing skyscraper. You wouldn't just start stacking bricks, right?

CAD stands for Computer-Aided Design. It's a type of software that helps you create robots, buildings, cars, or anything else you can think of, on a computer.

Using CAD, you can test out ideas, like changing the shape of a building or modeling a new rocket shape. You can even simulate how things will work, like seeing if a car's engine will fit under the hood.

Once you're happy with your design, you can send it to a 3D printer or a laser cutter.

Designers and Engineers are human superheroes with unique skills to improve the world. They created everything you see, hear, touch, and feel.

CAD is like having a superpower that lets you design and create anything you can imagine. So, let's master Tinkercad, a powerful tool that real architects, engineers, and designers use daily to bring their ideas to life.

Do Now: Student

If you are in a school:

1. Go to Tinkercad.com

2. Click **Login** in the top right corner

3. Select **Students with Class Code**

4. Enter the code your Instructor gave you and press **Go to my class**

5. Click **Create** then **3D Design**

Join Class

Type the code your teacher shared

Like: 123 456 789

Go to my class

Start Tinkering

How will you create your account?

Sign up with Email

G Sign in with Google

 Sign in with Apple

More sign in options...

If you are on your own:

1. Go to Tinkercad.com

2. Click **Sign Up** in the top right

3. Select **Create a personal account**

4. Create an account using one of the options

5. Click **Create** then **3D Design**

Dashboard ⌂

 The Tinkercad icon gets you back to the dashboard.

Access the Learning Center and Challenges via Resources.

You can also access the Gallery of public designs here.

This page is your Dashboard. Press the Tinkercad icon in the top left to get back to it.

Use the buttons on the left to access your Classes, Designs, Collections and more.

DO NOW

To create a new 3D Design press **+ Create** and then **3D Design** to open a 3D Workspace.

Access or delete your recent designs using this button.

Fantastic Gogo-Sango

This page is your 3D design workspace.

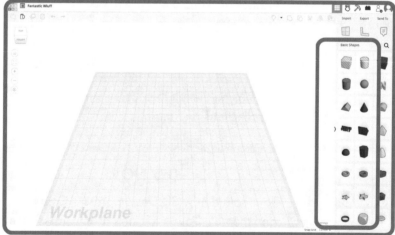

The Workplane is the blue grid in the middle.

The searchable library of pre-made shapes is on the right.

UI: Mouse

If you have a 3-button mouse, we recommend using it for Tinkercad for navigating the UI (User Interface).

Left click on the purple Cone and drag it onto the blue Workplane.

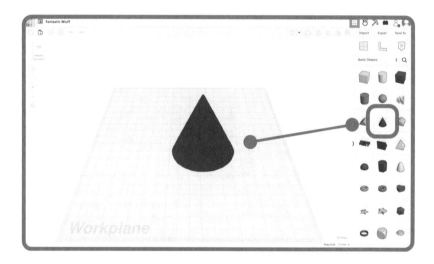

Next up, right-click and move the mouse. Did it **rotate** or **zoom in**?

....

Hold the mouse wheel and drag the mouse side to side. Does this **zoom out** or **pan** side-to-side?

....

UI: Touchpad

The touchpad is an alternative to the mouse and is found in the center of your laptop, below your keyboard. They all work differently so you may need to experiment to figure it out.

Click on the purple cone and drag it onto the blue Workplane.

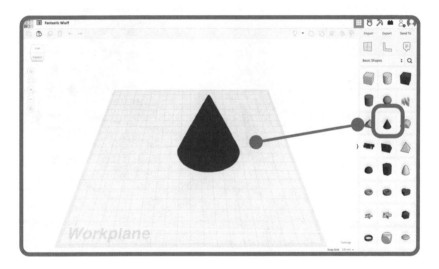

Touch the touchpad with 2 fingers and pinch in. Did it **rotate** or **zoom out**?

....

Press and hold with 2 fingers and move side to side. Does this **zoom out** or **orbit** around?

....

Drag the purple Cone onto the blue Workplane.

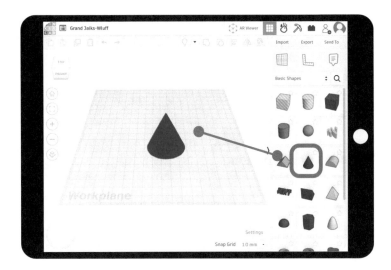

Tap the screen with 2 fingers and pinch closed. Did it **rotate** or **zoom out**?

....

Press and move side to side with 2 fingers. Does this **zoom out** or **pan** side-to-side?

....

New Design

Congratulations, the cone in the workspace is your first 3D Design!

Whenever you see this box, you need to save your work and start a new 3D Design.

Save it
Name it "CADclass 1"

1. Click in the name box in the top-left.

2. Type in "CADclass 1" and press enter on the keyboard.

3. Click the Tinkercad logo in the top left to return to the dashboard.

4. Start a new 3D Design.

Place It

Welcome to Tinkercad, where creative projects start by placing simple shapes!

Click and drag the red Box from the library on the right-hand side onto the blue Workplane.

PLAY

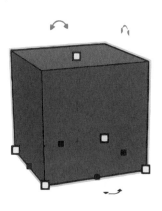

Click and drag the **White Boxes** surrounding the cube. What happened!?!

....

But wait, there's more! Hold down the Shift key, then click, hold, and drag those same White Boxes. What was different?

....

PLAY

Ready for the next trick... click, hold and drag **Black Squares.** Tell me what *that* did:

....

One more thing! Click, hold and drag the **Black Cone.** What directions did the cube go?

....

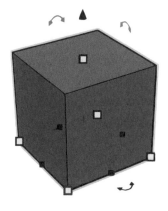

Did you catch that surprise when you clicked on a shape? A special box popped up called the Dialogue Box, filled with buttons, icons and sliders! Time to play around, transforming those shapes by pushing, pulling, and stretching.

PLAY

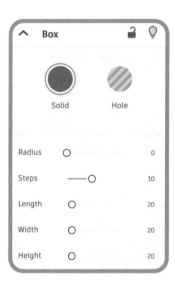

With the same red Box selected click, hold and drag the sliders in the Dialogue Box.

You can also type numbers into the boxes on the right! Let's make a quick smartphone:

Radius: 1.0 mm
Steps: 5
Length: 147.6 mm
Width: 71.6 mm
Height: 7.8 mm

DO NOW

Save your work and start a new 3D Design following the steps on the New Design page.

Save it
Name it "CADclass Phone" ⊓

Place It

PLAY

Start a new 3D Design. Click and drag in an orange Cylinder. **Zoom In** using the mouse scroll wheel or pinching open, and take a close look!

Q: Is it a smooth sided Cylinder or is it a polygon with many sides? Write C or P in the circle

---

But there are more tricks to explore! Let's go Cruising using Cruise mode. This feature lets you slide shapes onto other shapes and attach them as if they were magnetic.

PLAY

Press, hold, and drag the purple Cone onto the orange Cylinder but don't let go.

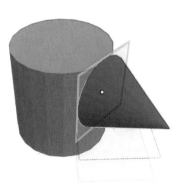

Move the Cone around the Cylinder and notice how it stays attached!

This is Cruise mode.

Release the mouse to place it. To re-activate cruise mode, click the shape, press C or the Cruise icon, and drag the white dot.

Place It

DO NOW

Save your work and start a new 3D Design following the steps on the New Design page.

Save it
Name it "CADclass Cruise"

1

CHALLENGE

Stack all the basic shapes (except Scribble) into your own balancing tower as fast as you can! How many seconds did it take?

Match the Icon + Word

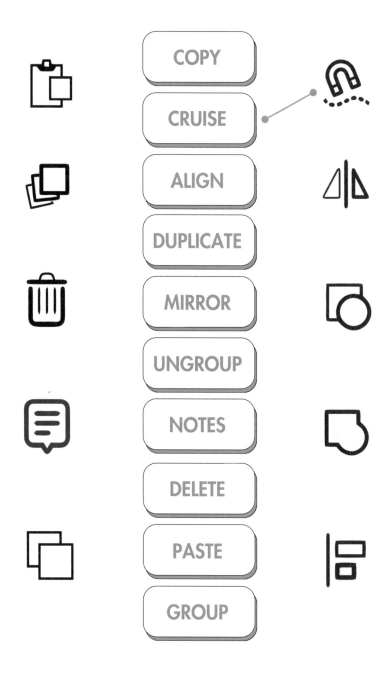

COPY

CRUISE

ALIGN

DUPLICATE

MIRROR

UNGROUP

NOTES

DELETE

PASTE

GROUP

Number the Features

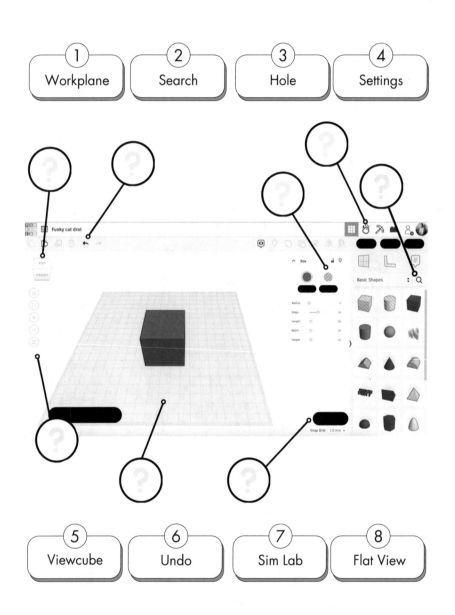

1 Workplane

2 Search

3 Hole

4 Settings

5 Viewcube

6 Undo

7 Sim Lab

8 Flat View

Move It »»

Moving shapes onto and around the Workplane is a key skill. It's like setting up a board game and then moving the pieces with confidence. You can Move with your mouse, trackpad, and keyboard.

DO NOW

From the Dashboard, search the gallery using the 🔍 in the top right corner for "*CADclass Compass*". Press **Copy and Tinker** to open it.

Copy and Tinker

You may see a message that says you can only see Staff Picks. This is because your class is in Safe Mode. Could you ask your instructor to change the setting on your Tinkercad Class page?

Safe Mode ✅

PLAY

Place the pink half Sphere to cover East [E]. Click and drag it to cover North [N]. What are the coordinates in mm shown on screen? e.g. 0.0 , 0.0 mm

....

Move It >>>

PLAY

While moving shapes with the mouse, hold down the Shift key. What happens?

....

Shapes can be moved using the arrow keys on your keyboard. To adjust the distance of movement, modify the **Snap Grid** below the **Settings** button.

Q: Can shapes be moved in 2 or 3 dimensions? Write your answer in the circle.

Save it
Name it "Compass"

2

CHALLENGE

What is the fewest arrow key presses can you move the pink Half Sphere in to cover?
N > E > S > W ?

Move It ⟫⟫⟫

Let's quickly talk about 2D and 3D: 2D flat shapes only have length and width, no thickness. 3D shapes have 3 dimensions: length, width, and thickness.

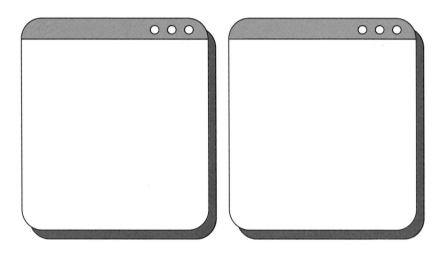

DO NOW

From the Dashboard, search the Gallery 🔍 for "CADclass XYZ axis" and press **Copy and Tinker**.

Copy and Tinker

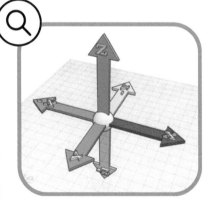

Move It >>>

PLAY

Practice moving the whole group in the X and Y axes using both of these:

1. Keyboard arrow keys
2. Mouse + Shift

The black cone lets you move shapes in the Z axis: above, below, or through the Workplane. Practice moving in the Z axis using:

3. The black cone

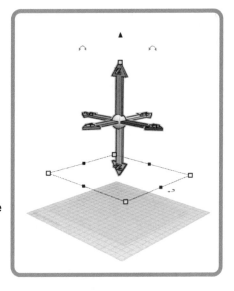

PLAY

Try the **Undo** and **Redo** actions.

Press Ctrl+Z to **Undo** an action and Ctrl+Y to **Redo** it.

There are also **Undo** and **Redo** buttons in the top left.

PLAY

Press **D** on the keyboard to "**Drop**" a part moved from the Workplane back onto to the Workplane.

Save it
Name it "[your name] XYZ Axis"

View It ∞

DO NOW

Search and add the "Printable Dice" from the Shapes Library.

Q: Two numbers are missing from the Dice. Write the total here:

PLAY

Click on a shape. Find the lightbulb icon in the Dialogue Box. Press it. What just happened?

3

CHALLENGE

Add the missing numbers to the Dice using the Text tool.

....

Bring it back using:
Ctrl + Shift + H or the press drop-down menu next to the lightbulb icon.

View It ⌾⌾

The Viewcube is navigation tool. You can move it and the Workplane moves, or, you can move the Workplane and the Viewcube moves. It has clickable faces, edges and vertices (corners).

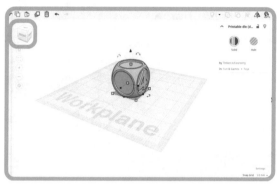

PLAY

Click the Right face.

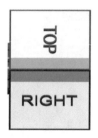

Click the Top/Right edge.

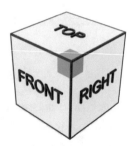

Click the Top / Front/Right vertex.

Q: Add up the number of edges, faces, and vertices a cube has and write it here

View It ⚭

Sometimes its better not to use your mouse to navigate around your 3D model. The View Buttons on the lefthand side of the screen are handy shortcuts.

DO NOW

Click each one of the View Buttons and describe what each does.

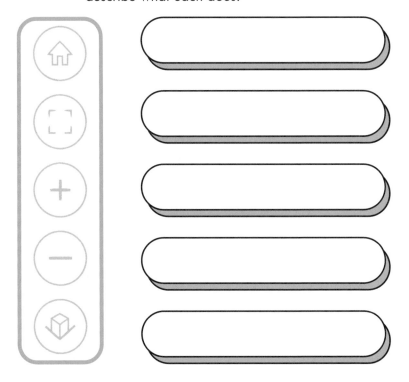

Save it
Name it "[your name] Printable Dice"

DO NOW

Press the recent designs button, then select New Design.

View It 👓

DO NOW

Go to the shape library and click the Basic Shape dropdown to show all the categories. Then click on Structures & Scenery and drag in the Apartment Building Ground Floor.

PLAY

Use your mouse and the View Buttons to:

1. **Zoom In**
2. **Fit All In View**
3. **Zoom Out**

PLAY

Click on the Top-Front-Right vertex then Fit All In View.

Toggle between the **Perspective / Flat** view.

What happens to the part of the design furthest away when in **Perspective View**?

....

Q: Count the total number of panes of glass the Apartment Building Ground Floor has.

Tinkercad is great on an iPad too, but you'll need to master some different moves to get the most out of it.

PLAY

Tap on an object. Then tap it again. This selects it, then unselects it.

Press the screen with 1 finger and drag to **Orbit**.

PLAY

Tap on an object, then another, and then another. This adds them to the selection.

Press and move with 2 fingers to **Pan**.

PLAY

Tap on an object. Tap and hold the button in the bottom left. This is an action modifier. For example, to change the scale from the center.

PLAY

Double tap, hold, and drag to create a selection box.

Pinch open or closed to **Zoom In** or **Zoom Out**.

View It: iPad

Tinkercad on the iPad has one more special trick, Augmented Reality (AR)! Press the AR Viewer button and place your digital design into a physical space.

AR is a technology that maps digital information onto the real world.

It's used in applications like gaming, watching movies, and navigation.

PLAY

Search the **Gallery** for a pair of headphones.

Copy and Tinker It.

Use the **AR Viewer** to place it in your room.

Pinch the object to scale it.

Rotate It ↻

In Tinkercad, you can move shapes along 3 axes (X, Y, and Z).

Shapes can move left/right, up/down, and forward/backward.

They can also rotate around each axis. These make up the 6 DOFs (Degrees of Freedom).

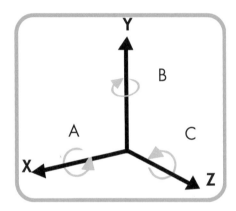

If you want to drive a screw into a piece of wood, it must move in 2 DOFs. It must travel into the wood while also rotating around the same axis.

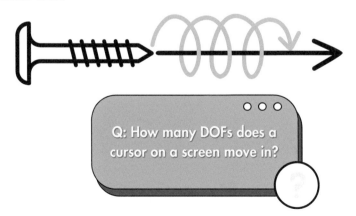

Q: How many DOFs does a cursor on a screen move in?

Rotate It C

When a shape is selected, notice the 3 curved arrows. Each represents a different axis to spin your shape around. Click and drag one, and your shape will rotate.

DO NOW

Save your previous design and start a new 3D Design.

Find the "Block head" model by searching for it or via the **Creatures & Characters** dropdown.

Drag it onto the **Workplane**.

PLAY

You'll see 3 curved arrows when the shape is selected.

Click, hold, and move each arrow to rotate in each axis to nod, tilt, and shake his head!

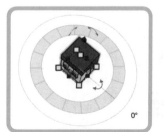

Notice the **Protractor** that appears when rotating.

This gives you more control over how much it turns.

Rotate It ⟳

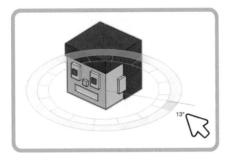

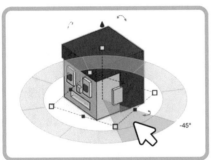

PLAY

Look closely! What happens differently when your mouse pointer is inside versus outside the **Protractor**?

....

....

○ ○ ○

Q: When rotating, hold Shift. How many degrees does the Protractor snap to?

Save it
Name it "Rotate It"

Rotate It ↻

Tinkercad also has its own museum of wonders called the Gallery. There are many designs that you can use and remix. Find the Gallery via the Dashboard in the top right-hand corner using the 🔍.

> Search 3D Designs and more... 🔍

DO NOW

Search the gallery for "CADclass rotate"and press **Copy and Tinker** to make a copy.

> Copy and Tinker

4

CHALLENGE

How long (in seconds) does it take you to rotate the cubes so all the sides have the same colors?

?

Save it
Name it "Speed Cube"

Size It

It's essential to resize/scale shapes to explore form and proportion or to make your designs fit with other objects.

DO NOW

Create a new 3D Design and drag in a Polygon. Select it.

Click on and test each of these symbols. Describe what they do in the box.

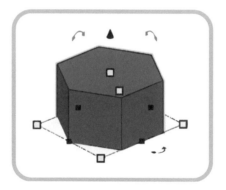

DO NOW

Try holding **Shift** while trying some of these actions to see if there is anything different.

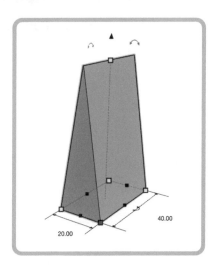

DO NOW

You can also resize shapes to a specific dimension by typing a number into the dimension box.

Drag a Roof onto the **Workplane** and make it:

- 20.0 mm wide
- 40.0 mm deep
- 60.0 mm tall

PLAY

Start a new 3D Design. Drag in a blue Sphere and make a few copies.

Click on the white or black handles and a dimension box pops up. Type in any number.

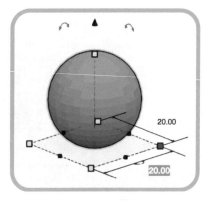

Play with all the resizing options to make a pile of magic stones!

Save it
Name it "Size It"

Size It

White handles let you resize in 2 directions simultaneously, while the black handles only let you resize one side at a time.

Action modifier buttons add superpowers: Shift and Alt (or option). On an iPad, this is the white button in the screen's bottom left corner.

DO NOW

Create a new 3D Design. Change the view so you can look down on the Workplane from above. Click and drag the orange Tube into place so it frames the letter W.

PLAY

Select the Tube, hold **Shift**, and drag the white square. Notice the direction the Tube scales in.

PLAY

Press Undo. Repeat the action but hold Shift + Alt / option and drag a white square. You can still see the letter W because it scaled from the center, not one side.

DO NOW

Open a new 3D Design.

Go to the library and use the top dropdown menu to find **Creatures & Characters**.

Use the arrows on the first sub-menu to scroll across. Select **Animals**. ◄►

Use your searching, moving, and resizing skills to attempt Challenge 5.

5
CHALLENGE

Create an alliterated zoo of strangely scaled animals: a flat frog, a big bee, a long llama, a stretched seal...

Save it
Name it "Animal Zoo"

Fill in the Shortcut Gaps

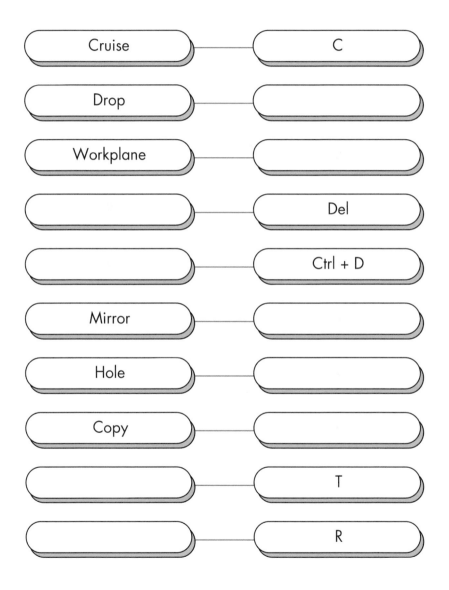

Cruise	C
Drop	
Workplane	
	Del
	Ctrl + D
Mirror	
Hole	
Copy	
	T
	R

Group It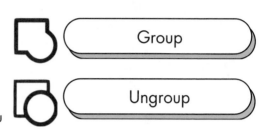

The Group tool combines shapes into new objects. If one of those shapes is a Hole, it removes material from the other shape(s). These are the 2 buttons you need:

Group

Ungroup

Q: Hover your mouse over the Group button. Ctrl + ? is the shortcut key for Group?

PLAY

Create a new 3D Design.

Drag a red cube onto the **Workplane** and place a blue Sphere on top of it.

Resize the Sphere to be 28 mm in all directions.

Move the Sphere so it's inside the cube.

Select both shapes (hold Shift while clicking) and press **Group**.

Now you have a new object!

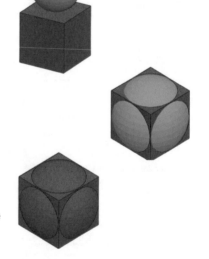

Save it
Name it "Convex Cube"

1. Create a new 3D Design. Search for "Signet Ring Blank" and drag it onto the Workplane.

2. Drag text onto the ring, change it to your initials, and resize it.

3. Select and move the Text down through the ring surface with ▲.

4. Select both shapes by holding Shift when clicking and **Group** them. Note the blue outline on both selected objects.

5. Now you have a ring with "embossed" letters.

6. When you grouped the shapes they might have changed color to match the first part selected. To keep the original colors click **Solid** > then **Multicolor**.

Save it
Name it "[name] Ring"

Copy It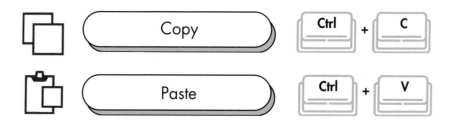

Like in other software, you can make copies of all or part of your designs using standard Copy and Paste keyboard shortcuts.

Copy		**Ctrl** + **C**
Paste		**Ctrl** + **V**

DO NOW

Go to the Gallery, search 🔍 for "CADclass alphabet", and press **Copy and Tinker**.

Do your letters look a bit wonky?

Don't worry, we'll be exploring how to line them up using the **Align** tool soon.

PLAY

Practice **Copy** and **Pasting** letters – keep the alphabet and create the word TINKERCAD.

Try to use both the onscreen buttons and and the keyboard shortcuts.

Copy It ⧉

DO NOW

Open a new 3D Design. Find one of these figures from the Creatures & Characters dropdown menu in the Library and drag it onto the Workplane.

PLAY

Practice using the keyboard arrow keys to move the figure left and right.

Edit the distance the character moves with each click by changing the **Snap Grid** to 5.0 mm.

Off
0.1 mm
0.25 mm
0.5 mm
1.0 mm
2.0 mm
5.0 mm
Brick

Snap Grid 1.0 mm ▲

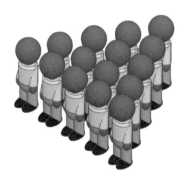

6

CHALLENGE

Use a character to make a triangle using only Copy + Paste + Move.

What is the fewest clicks you can do it in?

Duplicate It

The Duplicate tool is similar to the Copy tool, but with a twist. It remembers your last move and mimics it. So, not only does it copy and paste selected objects, but it also repeats your previous action.

DO NOW

1. Start a new 3D Design.
2. Find and insert a Star.
3. Select the shape.
4. Click **Duplicate**.
5. **Rotate** it and move it.
6. Click **Duplicate** repeatedly.

Insert and select Star

PLAY

Create a spiral staircase from a single resized box.

💡 Don't forget to move in all 3 axes and rotate too!

Press **Duplicate** and move the Star

○ ○ ○

Q: Ctrl + ? is the shortcut key for Duplicate?

Save it
Name it "Duplicate It"

Press **Duplicate** again and again...

Hide It 💡

Sometimes you'll want to hide shapes rather than delete them forever. Maybe there's too much design magic happening on the screen. Don't get rid of it, hide it!

DO NOW

Search the gallery for "CADclass 16 segment display" and press **Copy and Tinker** to make a copy.

Copy and Tinker

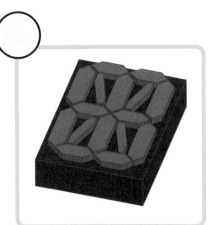

PLAY

Practice selecting segments by:

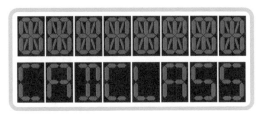

1. Holding **Shift** and clicking shapes to select multiple segments.

2. Using the **Hide** tool, try to create your name.

Note: If you accidentally select the wrong segment, keep holding Shift and press it again to deselect it.

Save it
Name it "16 Segment"

Other times, you'll want something in between Solid and Hidden. Go into the color menu and find the **Transparent** checkbox, or use the keyboard shortcut **T** to make it look like water or glass.

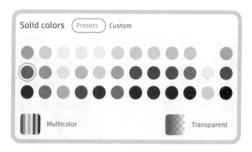

The Shell Game is a trick often seen in performances and at fairs involving a ball and 3 cups. In this game, a player must guess which cup the ball is under. The operator manipulates the game to deceive the player, often using sleight of hand.

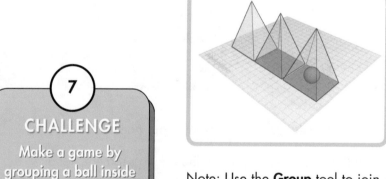

7

CHALLENGE

Make a game by grouping a ball inside one of 3 shapes. Show it using transparency. Jumble them & unhide to reveal it.

Note: Use the **Group** tool to join the ball and its Pyramid so they move together.

Using the Align tool or the keyboard shortcut L, you can bring 2 or more shapes into perfect alignment. It works in all 3 dimensions (X, Y, Z).

DO NOW

1. Start a new 3D Design.

2. Grab a Cylinder and make it 50.0 x 50.0 mm wide and 20.0 mm in height.

3. Grab a Cone and drag it roughly onto the top face of the Cylinder. Make it 50.0 x 50.0 mm wide and 30.0 mm tall.

4. Select both objects and press the **Align** button.

5. Click the middle ● on the Workplane and notice how the Cone aligns to the center of the Cylinder.

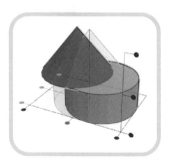

6. Press **Undo** and select both shapes again.

7. Press the top ● on the Z (↑ ↓) axis first and it'll align to the top of the Cone. The order of operation is very important!

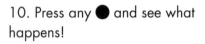
8. Click **Undo**, re-select both shapes, and click **Align**.

9. Click the Cylinder *again* - this makes it a reference, and you'll notice the alignment nodes ● are only surrounding it, so it will not move.

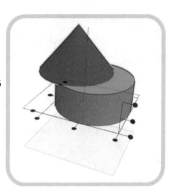

10. Press any ● and see what happens!

PLAY

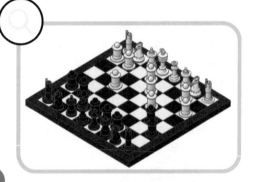

Search the gallery for "CADclass chess!" and press **Copy and Tinker** to open the design.

Copy and Tinker

8

CHALLENGE

Hold the Shift key while selecting a moved piece and an unmoved pawn of the same color, then use Align to reset the game.

Knowledge check

Refresher:

Sketch the **Duplicate** icon here

Refresher:

Sketch the **Ungroup** icon here

Q: Ctrl + ? is the shortcut key for Hide?

Refresher:

Sketch the **Un/Hide** icon here

Refresher:

Sketch the **Copy** icon here

Until now, you've been creating by adding parts, like building with blocks. But you can also create by subtracting using Holes. This tool removes material from a solid when grouped. Holes are striped, grey, and semi-transparent.

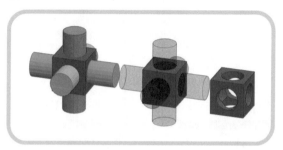

DO NOW

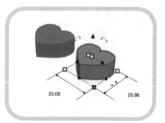

1. Start a new 3D Design.
2. Drag in a Heart shape from the Gallery and Copy & Paste it so there are 2.
3. Resize one so it's 3.0 mm less in both the X and Y axes.
4. Make it a **Hole**.
5. **Align** and **Group** them to make a heart-shaped cookie cutter! ●

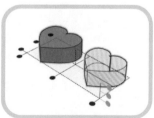

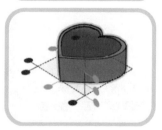

Q: Can ANY shape become a hole? Y or N

Rename

Q: Hey Tinkercad, what's with the weird names?

A: Tinkercad automatically generates a unique 3-word name so files don't get mixed up. You can change it using one of these methods.

DO NOW

Double click on the name and delete it. Update it with something that identifies your name, what it is, and the version:

Ed_cookiecutter_heart_V1

PLAY

You can also rename your design via the Dashboard.

Get there by pressing the Tinkercad logo in the top left corner.

Then press the gear icon in the top right of the preview tile, select Properties, and change the name.

Use one of your existing designs to practice this.

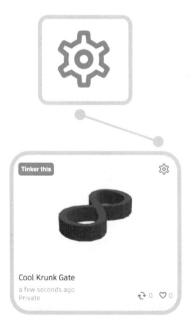

Search Shapes Q

Searching for pre-made shapes is at the heart of Tinkercad. This tool allows you to find and use hundreds of models that would otherwise take hours or days to create.

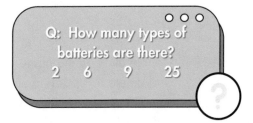

○ ○ ○
Q: How many types of batteries are there?
2   6   9   25

?

What is the BIGGEST and the *smallest* design you can find in the library (if it was real)?

○ ○ ○
Q: What is the theme of the OMSI collection? (A) Furniture (B) Space (C) Construction.

?

....

....

9

CHALLENGE

Create a tiny desert island using only shapes from the Library?

Mirror

You've gone left and right, up and down. Now let's go back-to-front, over-and-over! Mirror allows you to flip your design using the black arrows that appear when you click the Mirror icon.

Circle all the symmetrical letters :

A B C D E F G H I
J K L M N O P Q R
S T U V W X Y Z

List some symmetrical numbers 1-100:

Q: What is is the shortcut key for Mirror?

Use the **Text** tool and write MOM.

Change the font to sans to remove the serifs (the little tails on the letters shown in the image to the left).

Mirror the word and find the hidden word. What is it?

....

10

Q **CHALLENGE**

Find an asymmetrical object from the Gallery and "animate it" by quickly Mirroring it.

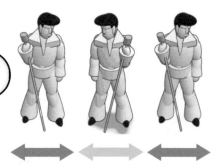

Save it
Name it "Mirror"

Match the Icon & Word

COPY

CRUISE

HOLE

DUPLICATE

ALIGN

UNGROUP

VIEWCUBE

UN/HIDE

PASTE

GROUP

Use the Grid

Grids help you visualize the distance between shapes, like squares on graph paper. Snap Grid changes the spacing of those squares on your Workplane. When the Snap Grid is on, shapes align to the lines. You can change the spacing and turn the Grid on/off via the button in the bottom right corner.

DO NOW

1. Change the **Snap Grid** to 5.0 mm spacing.

2. Create 1 white cube 25.0 x 25.0 x 25.0 mm.

3. Create 1 black cube 25.0 x 25.0 x 25.0 mm.

4. **Align** the black and the white cube

Off
0.1 mm
0.25 mm
0.5 mm
1.0 mm
2.0 mm
5.0 mm
Brick

Snap Grid 1.0 mm ▲

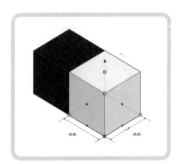

11

CHALLENGE

Make a chess board using the keyboard keys by Copy & Pasting 2 cubes at the same time.
Hint: Copy + Paste + → ← ↑ ↓ + M.

Number the Features

1 Flat View	2 Shadow	3 Solid	4 Collaborate

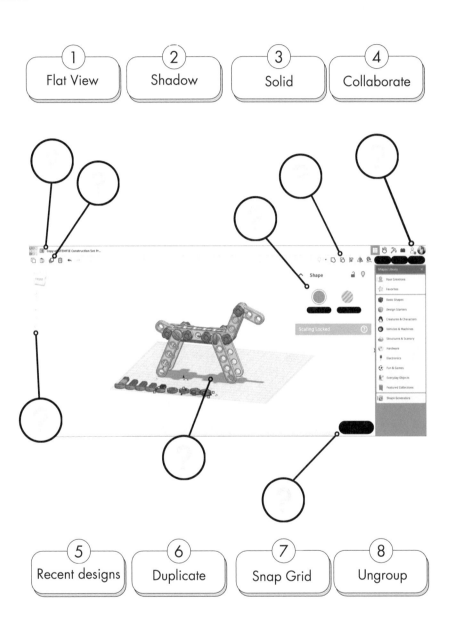

5 Recent designs	6 Duplicate	7 Snap Grid	8 Ungroup

Workplanes

A Workplane is like a piece of paper you place on the surface of a shape to connect another shape to its surface. Cruise mode automatically does this when you drag in a new shape, but you can add more yourself!

DO NOW

1. Drag the Icosahedron onto the Workplane.

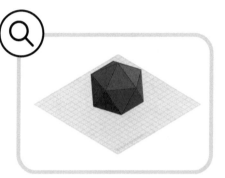

2. Scale it to approximately a quarter of the Workplane, keeping its proportions.

HINT: use the Action Modifier keyboard key.

PLAY

3. Drag and scale other shapes onto the Icosahedron to create a fun character.

Check out the free trial video by HL Mod Tech on the CADclass website!

http://cadclass.org/courses/tinkercad

Sometimes aligning objects is tricky so let's look at how you can use Workplanes to help.

1. Drag a Box on to the Workplane and make it orange.

2. Resize it to: 19.7 x 28.6 x 13.1 mm.

3. Copy and Paste it to make a duplicate and make it blue.

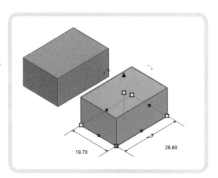

4. Align the Boxes using the **Align** tool.

5. Now Align them using the mouse keys and the Snap Grid.

When you Zoom in you'll see you always have a gap or an overlap because of the tricky dimensions.

6. Press **W** for Workplane and place new Workplane on the side of the orange Box.

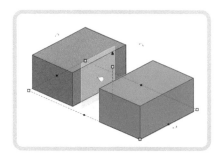

Workplanes

7. Select the other Box and press **D** to drop the blue Box onto the new Workplane.

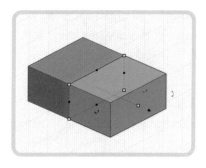

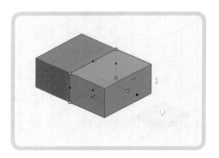

8. Press **W** again and place the Workplane back on the original Workplane. The new one will disappear

9. Zoom In to check for a gap or overlap.

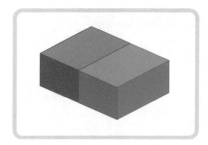

Save it
Name it "Aligned"

Measure It

You know how to size objects with the black and white handles and the dimension box. But what if you need to know specific measurements? The Ruler is the tool you'll need.

- Find the Micro:bit in the **Shape Library** and drag it onto the Workplane.
- Click the **Ruler** and place it away from the bottom left corner.
- Select the Micro:bit to measure it.

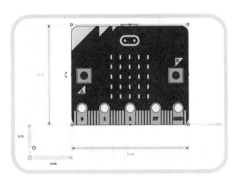

The blue dimensions are **absolute** to the part.

The green dimensions are **relative** to the origin of the Ruler.

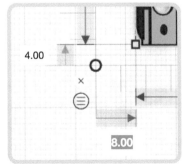

1. Place the Ruler near the bottom corner of the Micro:bit.
2. Select the Micro:bit and change the green dimensions (relative) to 0.0 mm to snap its corner to the origin.
3. Check the Micro:bit width and height. Check your answers here: en.wikipedia.org/wiki/Micro_Bit

Measure It

With the Ruler placed and the Micro:bit selected, press the circle with 3 lines by the origin. This toggles the measurement from the **endpoint** to the **midpoint** of the object. Press **X** to close the Ruler.

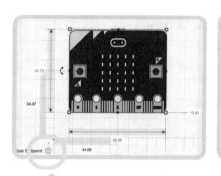 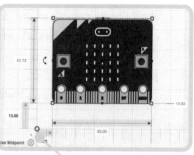

Save it
Name it "Micro:bit"

DO NOW

1. Start a new 3D Design.
2. Find the 9V battery and drag it in.

CHALLENGE

12

Measure its length, width, and height (to the top of the longest contact). Find the volume.

Scribble

The Scribble tool is your freestyle friend! Use it to break out of the polygon-based world of Basic Shapes and design something organic!

DO NOW

Find the **Scribble** button from the Basic Shapes library.

Click the Scribble button and notice the new interface.

PLAY

Try to write out a famous phrase in cursive writing.
Press the X in the preview window to close it and place the design on the Workplane.

Q: Is there a shortcut key for Scribble? Y or N

PLAY

Do a little research, why is this ↑ phrase famous?

....

....

Scribble

PLAY

Double click on the scribble design to reopen and edit it.

Use the **Erase** tool to get rid of parts of your design.

13

CHALLENGE

Find "boy standing, arms down."

Use the Scribble tool to design him some crazy hair.

PLAY

It can be tricky to Align a Scribble, so you may need to use the **Align** tool to place the hair on the head.

Q: Can a Scribble be used as a hole? Y or N

Save it
Name it "Scribble Hair"

Paste It 📋

Not only can you duplicate shapes inside a design, but you can also copy and paste them between 2 browser tabs. Open Tinkercad in 2 tabs. In one open and Copy any design, then move to the second tab, and Paste it in.

Example:

Design A
(**Copy** this: Ctrl+C)

Design B
(**Paste** A into this: Ctrl+V)

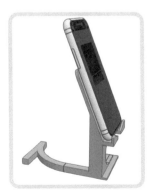

Design A _in_ Design B

Search the gallery for "CADclass RACKET" and in a different tab for "CADclass DIN". **Copy and Tinker** with both of them.

Design A

Design B

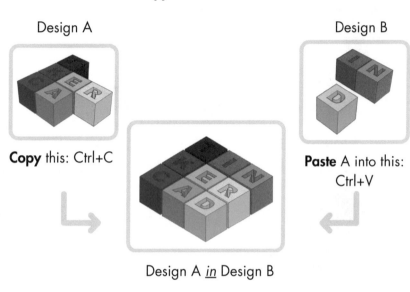

Copy this: Ctrl+C

Paste A into this: Ctrl+V

Design A _in_ Design B

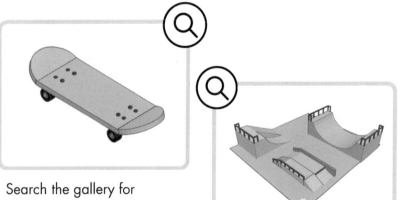

Search the gallery for "CADclass skateboard" then **Copy and Tinker** it.

In another tab search the gallery for "CADclass skate park" then **Copy and Tinker** it.

14

CHALLENGE

Combine 'CADclass skateboard' and 'CADclass skate park' into a new design. Resize and position the board on a ramp.

Save it
Name it "Skate Park"

Write the Term in the Box

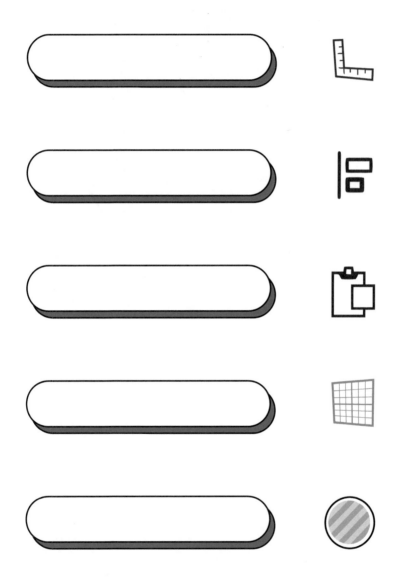

Import ⬇

3D Designs you find online are likely in STL or OBJ format. These are common types of 3D design files, like MP4 or WAV for music. You can Import these into Tinkercad to use or modify them.

DO NOW

Visit one of these 3D design repositories and find and save a "3DBenchy" STL or OBJ :

printables.com
thingiverse.com
thangs.com

PLAY

Press the **Import** button and import your 3DBenchy.

Import

When you import you can match the original designs units and alter scale and dimensions.

Import 3D Shape ×

3dbenchy (1).stl
10.76 MB

Units — Choose the unit of measurement the file was created with to get the correct scale in Tinkercad.

Millimeters | Inches

Scale (%) — 100

Dimensions
Length 31 Width 60 Height 48

Cancel | Import

2D vector graphics are common, often free online, and fun to play with in Tinkercad. You can Import and use them in many ways.

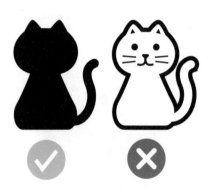

DO NOW

Visit svgrepo.com, or another source of Scalable Vector Graphics (SVG) files.

Find and save a solid SVG of an animal, and **Import** it.

Scale if necessary.

PLAY

Click on the shape and change these settings using the Dialogue Box:

1. **Fill mode** to > **Outer Line.**
2. **Corners** > **Rounded.**
3. **Line Width** > 3.0 mm.

You have a cookie cutter!

Save it
Name it "Cookie Cutter"

Laser Cut

Laser cutters work like knives, slicing materials such as wood and plastic using focused light. You can use Tinkercad to generate SVG files that can be used as a path for a laser cutter.

An SVG is the generated profile where a design intersects (goes through) the **Workplane.** All you need to do is press **Export** and select **SVG.**

<table>
<tr><td>Export</td><td>.SVG</td></tr>
</table>

PLAY

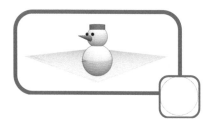

Find an object that changes profile along its Z axis (e.g. a one, snowman, or a mountain).

Move the shape ▲ so it intersects the **Workplane,** press **Export**, and then **SVG.**

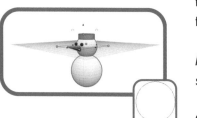

Move the shape and repeat the steps above.

Go to: <u>t.ly/HMzxO</u> to view your SVGs.

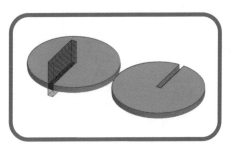

15

CHALLENGE

Create an SVG for a snowflake that can be slotted together from 2x 3.0 mm thick laser cut parts.

Save it
Name it "Snowflake"

Sort the file types

OBJ | STL | SVG

2D	3D
e.g. PDF	

Export & 3D Print

3D printers make real objects from digital designs. Most 3D printers use a heated extruder that melts plastic filament and builds up the model layer by layer. It's a magic machine that creates something from nothing!

DO NOW

Open your brick design.

Navigate to and press **Export** then **STL**.

Export

.STL

The 3D model starts as a digital Tinkercad design. It's then exported as an STL or OBJ.

The STL is cut into layers in a slicer program. These layers are converted into G-code, a language that a 3D printer can understand.

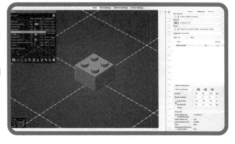

Filament and the G-code are fed into the machine where your model will come into reality!

Export & Send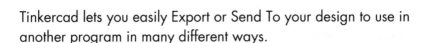

Tinkercad lets you easily Export or Send To your design to use in another program in many different ways.

DO NOW

Open any of your saved designs and find and press the **Export** and **Send To** buttons. Explore the options.

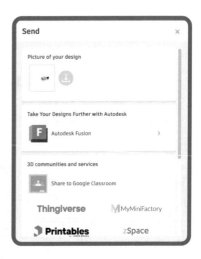

Check the 4 file types you can Export:

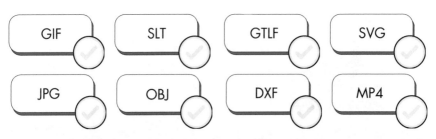

GIF SLT GTLF SVG

JPG OBJ DXF MP4

Export & Send ✉

Tinkercad is made by Autodesk. Its big brother, Fusion, is more powerful and has many customization options.

One of the Export links is called Send to Fusion, which sends your Tinkercad design straight to Fusion if you already have it installed and open.

If you are interested in learning Fusion, use this link to find out more

The Ultimate Online Fusion
CAD Class
CADclass.org

There are also many new AI-powered rendering tools (used to make digital designs more realistic). If you are interested, search for and try one with one of your Tinkercad creations.

Workspace Setup 🔧

Switch up the visual vibe of your Tinkercad workspace by pressing the Settings button to customize the look and feel!

DO NOW

Start a new 3D Design.

Find and press the **Settings** button located near the bottom right of the screen.

> Settings

Explore the options.

Workspace settings ✕

Background color

Show shadows ☐

Show grid ☐

Cruise when adding new shapes ☑

Zoom speed ───────○── Slow   Fast

Units   Millimeters (Default)   ▾

Presets   Custom (Default)   ▾
             Width   Length
             200   200

Make default

Close settings

Q: How many preset background colors are there?

255   21   12   36

PLAY

Find and press the **Presets** dropdown arrow.

Q: What do all the names in the presets refer to?
A: 3D Printers B: File types

Makerbot Replicator Z18

Makerbot Replicator 2

Type A Machines Series 1

Ultimaker Original+

Ultimaker 2+

Ultimaker 2 Go

Ultimaker 3

Workspace Setup

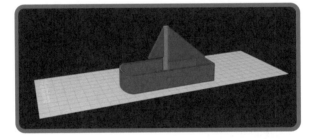

16

CHALLENGE

Design a boat and make the workplane a narrow river and the background a dark night.

PLAY

"**Make Default**" sets your next new designs **Workplane** to that size automatically. If you have a 3D printer or laser cutter, you could set the default to those bed dimensions.

PLAY

How else could you make the appearance of water for the river? (look at Hide It)

....

Save it
Name it "Night Boat"

Custom Shapes

Sometimes you'll want to make and/or save a shape that doesn't exist. The more custom shapes you save, the more complex your custom designs can be.

DO NOW

Find and select the **Shape Generators** button at the bottom of the parts library list.

PLAY

Find the "Pointed Windmill Blade" and select it.

Play with the variables!

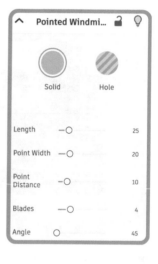

How to Design the Best Wind Farm Blade in Tinkercad
t.ly/PFGB-

Custom Shapes

Want something more specific? You'll need to create your own Custom Shape, which only takes a few simple steps. Begin by opening a new 3D Design to make a building brick.

1. Add and resize a Box to 8.0 x 8.0 x 9.6 mm.

2. **Cruise** a Cylinder onto the top face and make it 4.8 x. 4.8 x 1.7 mm.

3. **Align** then **Group** them together.

4. Make a **Copy**.

5. Create a **Workplane**, place it on the side of the original and drop (**D**) the **Copy** onto it. **Align** them.

6. Make this a **Group**, **Copy** & **Paste** it, and **Align** it.

HINT: look at the Workplanes chapter for help.

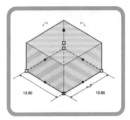

7. Add a new Box, make it 13.8 x 13.8 x 8.4 mm, and set it to be a Hole.

8. **Align** and **Group** to hollow out the solid.

9. Change the color, or make it **transparent** so you can see the internal details.

10. Find and select Your Creations.

11. Select **Create Shape** and click on your shape.

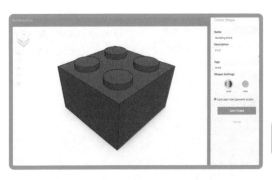

12. Give it a name, description, add tags, and lock the part size. Save it!

Save Shape

True or False?

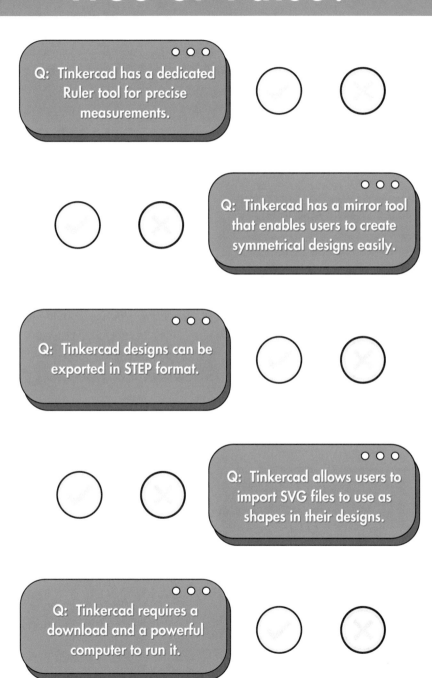

Q: Tinkercad has a dedicated Ruler tool for precise measurements.

Q: Tinkercad has a mirror tool that enables users to create symmetrical designs easily.

Q: Tinkercad designs can be exported in STEP format.

Q: Tinkercad allows users to import SVG files to use as shapes in their designs.

Q: Tinkercad requires a download and a powerful computer to run it.

Add Notes

Notes are a great way to leave messages for yourself and others. You'll find the Notes button above the Shapes menu, next to the Ruler and Workplane icons, or use the keyboard shortcut N.

DO NOW

Search the gallery and find a model of the solar system.

Use the **Notes** tool to label the planets.

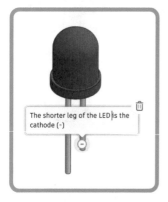

The shorter leg of the LED is the cathode (-)

Earth | Saturn | Jupiter
Mars | Venus | Uranus
Neptune | Mercury | The Sun

17

CHALLENGE

Find a model of a bicycle and label all its mechanisms e.g. chain, lever, bearing...

The Bicycle by Bartosz Ciechanowski
https://t.ly/PFGB-

Custom Colors

Sometimes, you'll like how Tinkercad makes things look; other times, you won't. To change your creations, you have two options: the Preset button or the Custom button!

DO NOW

Create a new shape made from many different objects.

Use the **Solid** button to make each shape a different color.

PLAY

Group it all together and notice how it changes to be a single color.

If you want every part to be a different color, press **Multicolor**.

Custom Colors

The **Custom** button allows you to make any color you want. You can pick a color, add your own RGB or HSB, or even enter a specific Hex code.

DO NOW

Go to
encycolorpedia.com/flags

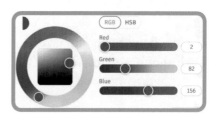

Use it to find the hex codes for a simple flag you like.

Make a note of them:

....
....

PLAY

Start a new 3D Design.
Recreate the geometry of the design.

This is the Icelandic flag geometry:

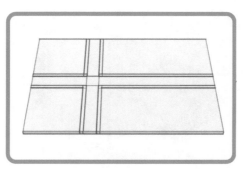

Custom Colors

For the Icelandic people, the flag's coloring represents a vision of their country's landscape. The colors stand for 3 of the elements that make up the island. Red is the fire produced by the island's volcanoes, white recalls the ice and snow that covers the land, and the blue is for the mountains of the island.
en.wikipedia.org/wiki/Flag_of_Iceland

PLAY

Select parts of the geometry, then apply the Hex or RGB codes using the **Custom** button to match the flag.

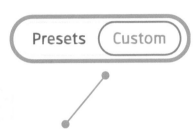

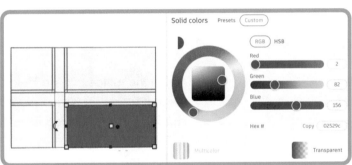

Solid colors   Presets   Custom

RGB   HSB

Red   2
Green   82
Blue   156

Hex #   Copy   02529c

Multicolor   Transparent

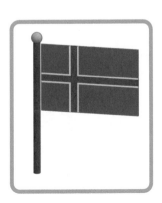

02529c

Save it
Name it "[country] Flag"

Colors can also be a gradient. Do this challenge, but pay close attention, it's tricky!

18

CHALLENGE

Create a complex shape with a gradient color

DO NOW

1. Search the gallery for a complex design like the "Aluminium Lattice Structure" by bethanytabiG9H7H and **Copy and Tinker** it.

2. Find a "gradient block" like Gradient Bumper Pack by ZDP189 and **Copy and Tinker** one of the blocks.

3. Resize the block so it's slightly bigger than the lattice. Make a **Copy** and change its color to **Solid**.

4. Set the lattice to be a **Hole, Align** it inside the solid colored shape, and then **Group** them.

5. Turn this new shape into a **Hole** and **Align** it with the gradient block.

6. **Group** them. Voila!

Blocks & Bricks

Can you brick it? Yes, you can! Press the **Blocks** or **Bricks** button to transform your design into blocks or bricks.

Tinker this

DO NOW

Find a "Soma Cube" puzzle in the gallery. Make a **Copy** to **Tinker It**.

Press the waffle icon whenever you want to get back to the 3D design space.

PLAY

Try to re-make it in both the blocks and bricks environments. Play with the design detail buttons to alter the brick/block size.

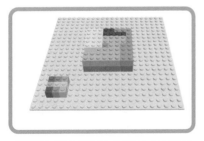

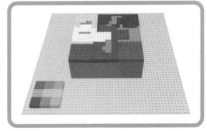

PLAY

Try the **Layers** button to get
layer-by-layer build instructions.

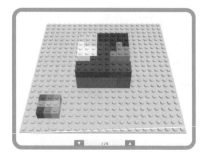

Q: Can you export a blocks
design as a .schemetic to load
into blocks software: Y or N?

Save it
Name it "Soma Cube"

Collaborate

Sharing is caring. Tap the Invite People button in the upper right corner to team up and share your work. Press Generate New Link to create a unique link. Links never expire, but the old one will stop working if you generate a new one.

Generate new link

When collaborating you'll only see the outcome of the collaborators work, not them moving their mouse or changing the view.

19

CHALLENGE

Create the lower bun of a burger. Share a link with a friend. Co-create a stacked burger, taking it in turns to add layers.

Sim Lab ☝

The **Sim Lab** is a magical 3D playground where you can tweak gravity, switch up materials, create joints, and throw objects! Tap the falling apple icon to dive in!

PLAY

In the 3D space create an aligned see-saw / teeter-totter like this.

Then press the **Sim Lab** icon and click one of the cubes.

Press the **Material** button and select a dense material like steel.

Press the **play** button in the bottom left corner to simulate it!

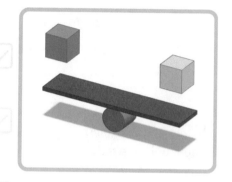

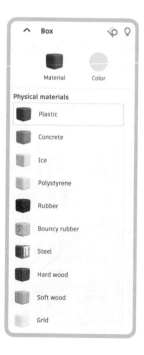

While the Sim is working press the left mouse button to throw stuff!

Press **Reset** to start over.

Sim Lab ✋

You can add Connectors to establish relationships between parts, allowing them to turn, twist, and slide. Let's look at the Axle, which creates a wheel-and-axle relationship between parts.

DO NOW

1.Start in the 3D space and recreate this design, **Aligning** the end of the red part to the center of the Cylinder.

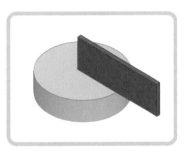

2. Navigate to the **Sim Lab** and place the **Axle Connector** (bottom right) on the top face of the Cylinder.

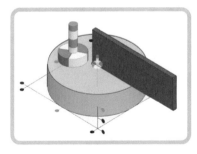

3. Go back to the 3D design space and make sure they are all **Aligned**.

4. Select the **Axle Connector** and drag the orange/white disc on onto the red part and the blue/white disc onto the blue part.

5. Back in the Sim Lab, press **Play** and click the left mouse to throw stuff and make the paddle spin!

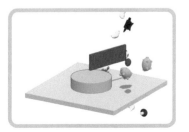

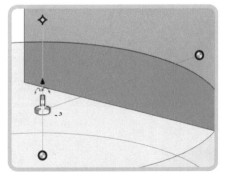

Number the Features

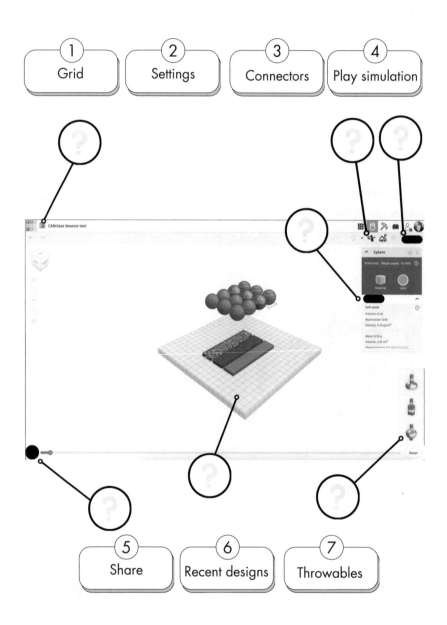

1 Grid

2 Settings

3 Connectors

4 Play simulation

5 Share

6 Recent designs

7 Throwables

Circuits 🔲

Now that you've explored 3D designs in Tinkercad, it's time to see what else is possible. Tinkercad Circuits is a virtual test lab for electronics like motors, lights, and sensors!

DO NOW

- Navigate to the dashboard.

- Press **+Create**.

- Press **Circuit** to open a new Circuit workspace.

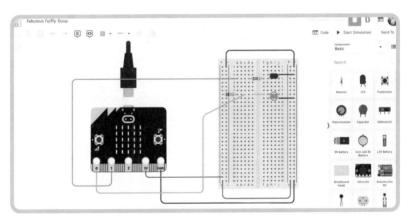

The **Circuits** workspace looks similar to the 3D workspace, with a searchable library on the right and buttons for different sub-workspaces on the top right.

Have a look around!

PLAY

Drag these components onto the workspace:
1. A resistor
2. An LED
3. A coin cell 3V battery
4. A slideswitch

Circuits

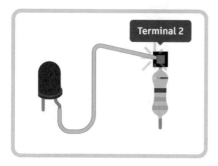

Click one of the legs of the LED. When you hover over it, it will tell you what it is.

Continue clicking to create a wire connection.

Join the wire to the top terminal of the resistor.

When it shows a red box, it's snapping to the end.

PLAY

Recreate this circuit.

Click on the resistor and use the Dialogue Box to change the value to 330 and the units from kΩ to Ω (kiloohms to ohms).

Notice how the color bands change.

Press the **Start Simulation** button, then press the switch to toggle it on/off.

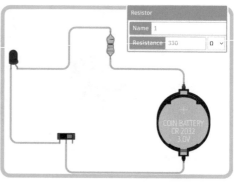

Remove the resistor and rewire the circuit. It exploded because there was too much current flowing into the LED, which wasn't protected by the resistor.

Circuits 🔲

To clear the Circuits workspace, press Ctrl + A (select all) on your keyboard, then press delete.

PLAY

Navigate to these 2 buttons in the top right.

One will create a schematic of your circuit and the other will provide a bill-of-materials (a shopping list).

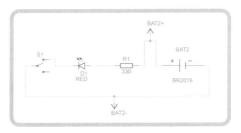

20
CHALLENGE

Create a circuit that turns a motor when near a light, using a photoresistor, a 9V battery and a hobby gear motor.

Micro:bits

You can also use, code, simulate, and link-to Micro:bits! These are small digital programmable microprocessors (computers) that can be used to edit and control real-world objects using Scratch-style coding.

DO NOW

Go to the drop down menu in the top right corner and select Micro:Bit.

Select the Analogue starter and drag it on to the workspace.

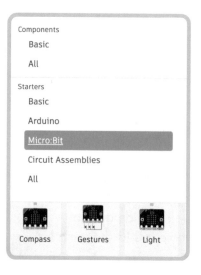

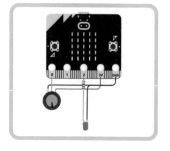

PLAY

Press the **Start Simulation** button then click and move to turn the Potentiometer dial in the bottom left.

This code creates a bar graph on the Micro:bit LED matrix and also lights up an external LED.

Micro:bits

DO NOW

Press **Stop Simulation** and then press **Code** to expand the Coding area.

Stop Simulation

This is where you can program the Micro:Bit using blocks or text-based programming.

</> Code

Minimize it by pressing the Code button again.

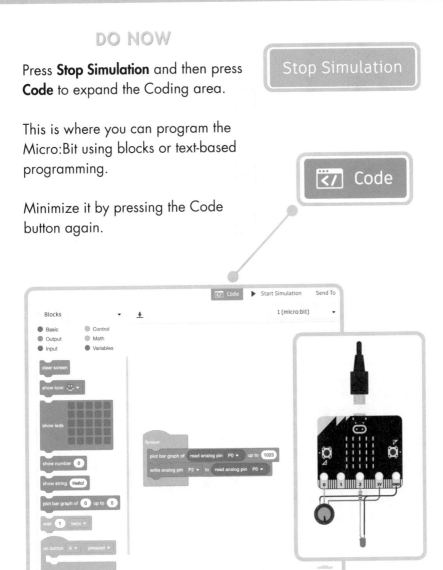

Micro:bits

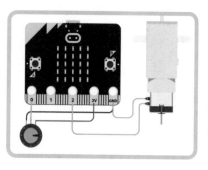

PLAY

Delete the LED and resistor and replace them with a HobbyGear motor.
Rewire it like in the image and re-start the simulation.

PLAY

If you want to learn more about Microbits go to tinkercad.com/learn and explore the **Circuits Micro:bits** tutorials.

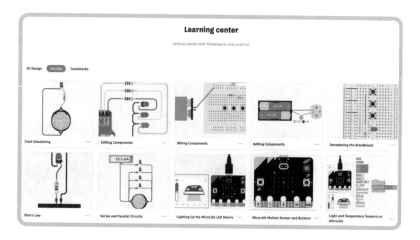

Learning center

Getting started with Tinkercad is easy and fun!

3D Design   Circuits   Codeblocks

Start Simulating   Editing Components   Wiring Components   Adding Components   Introducing the Breadboard

Ohm's Law   Series and Parallel Circuits   Lighting Up the Micro:bit LED Matrix   Micro:bit Motion Sensor and Buttons   Light and Temperature Sensors on Micro:bit

Save it
Name it "Micro:bit Motor"

Codeblocks </>

Codeblocks is a tool for creating 3D designs using drag-and-drop sections of code. Instead of typing out complicated commands, you can snap together Scratch-style Codeblocks to create designs. It's a fun and easy way to simultaneously program and design in 3D.

DO NOW

- Navigate to your dashboard page.

- Press **+Create.**

- Press **Codeblocks** to open a new Codeblock workspace.

The **Codeblocks** workspace looks familiar, but it has a coding workspace on the left and a 3D workspace on the right. You can resize the sides by holding and sliding the middle vertical bar. Additional action buttons are in the top right.

Codeblocks </>

DO NOW

Drag in these shapes.

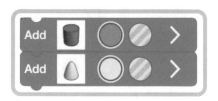

Press the **play** button in the top right.

Watch the code play and create.

Notice that the Paraboloid is hidden inside the Cylinder.

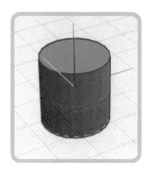

PLAY

Drag in these extra shapes then press the **play** button in the top right.

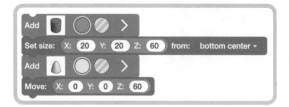

The purple block is modifying the previous shape. It sets the size and changes the location to the bottom center.

The second Move block shifts the Paraboloid to the top of the cylinder 60.0 mm up the Z axis.

Codeblocks </>

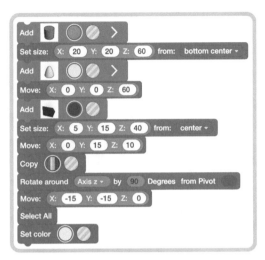

PLAY

Copy the rest of this code.

Then try to place the last 2 fins onto the base.

PLAY

To learn more about Codeblocks, visit tinkercad.com/learn and explore the Codeblocks tutorials.

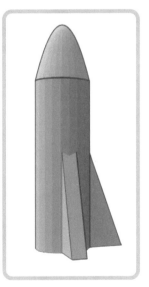

Save it
Name it "Codeblock Rocket"

Design Challenges

21
CHALLENGE

Design a storage container or desk organizer.

22
CHALLENGE

Recreate your bedroom, adding dream features & furniture in 3D!

23
CHALLENGE

In Sim Lab create the longest Rube Goldberg machine / marble run you can!

24
CHALLENGE

Design a Mars Rover in 3D and use Circuits to prototype a sensor circuit!

Math Challenges

25
CHALLENGE

Design a measuring tool, for example, a scoop to measure 10g volumes.

26
CHALLENGE

Create designs using basic shapes, e.g., a robot with 4 Boxes, 2 Spheres, etc.

27
CHALLENGE

Use geometric measurement, e.g., rotate an object by 145 degrees.

28
CHALLENGE

Design & 3D print a Maths tool, for example, a 60-degree triangular ruler.

Science Challenges

29 CHALLENGE

Physics: Design and test a Rube Goldberg machine.

30 CHALLENGE

Biology: Create and label a cross-section of a cell.

31 CHALLENGE

Chemistry: Recreate a representation of a molecule e.g. caffeine.

32 CHALLENGE

Design & 3D print a tool to help with a science experiment e.g. a test tube rack.

Engineering

33
CHALLENGE

Design and 3D print an egg-drop holder to protect the egg cargo.

34
CHALLENGE

Reverse Engineer and recreate an existing design e.g. a clothes pin / peg.

35
CHALLENGE

Design a rubber band powered car or a Pinewood Derby car.

36
CHALLENGE

Design and prototype a tool to help with an engineering project e.g. a multi-tool for a bicycle or robot.

Electronics

37
CHALLENGE
Design a plant watering system that detects dry soil and releases water.

38
CHALLENGE
Design a light-following robot using LDRs and DC motors.

39
CHALLENGE
Use a Micro:bit to create a safety light activated by movement and darkness.

40
CHALLENGE
Design a bedroom alarm that alerts you when someone walks in.

Art Challenges

41

CHALLENGE

Create an ambigram tessellation like MC Escher.

42

CHALLENGE

Recreate famous artwork, like a geometric Mondrian abstract or famous architecture, like Big Ben.

43

CHALLENGE

Create a recurring pattern based on inspiration from nature, e.g. honeycomb.

44

CHALLENGE

Use the Scribble tool to create profile to duplicate around a point to create a vase.

Social Studies

CHALLENGE

Create a famous building like the Leaning Tower of Pisa, or Eiffel Tower.

CHALLENGE

Design an assistive device that helps someone with a specific need or disability e.g. arthritis.

CHALLENGE

Create a famous landmark or geographic feature e.g. a volcano or a drainage basin.

CHALLENGE

Recreate a Greek or Roman architectural feature, e.g. a Doric column.

End of Book Quiz

1. Name a specific piece of 'everyday' CAD software (not Tinkercad).

2. Give a unique advantage of CAD when compared to creating designs using "traditional" hand tools like pencils and paper.

3. Explain the disadvantages of using CAD vs. designing with pencil and paper.

4. Describe 2 ways CAD could contribute to cost or time savings in design and manufacturing.

5. Explain some limitations you came up against when using Tinkercad.

6. How might Augmented Reality (AR) help consumers understand a product?

7. Name some benefits of designers using CAD that allow for collaboration with other designers.

8. Name the parts of a piece of clothing Tinkercad is well suited to design in 3D. Why is this?

9. State specific examples of types of products that Tinkercad is not well suited to designing in 3D. Why is this?

10. Name industries where CAD is commonly used and explain how it benefits these sectors.

11. Describe the relationship between CAD and CAM.

12. Discuss the potential security concerns associated with CAD data.

13. Explain the Sim Lab as if you were talking to a 5-year-old.

14. Is copy & paste the same as duplicate? Explain your answer.

15. In what way can keyboard shortcuts help a CAD designer?

16. Think up a question for your teacher/instructor:

Add a Definition

Align ....

Group ....

Ungroup ....

Mirror ....

Viewcube ....

Scribble ....

Export ....

Import ....

Cruise ....

Add a Definition

Pan ....

Orbit ....

Zoom ....

Workplane ....

Copy ....

Paste ....

Duplicate ....

Move ....

Rotate ....

Shortcuts

View the workspace

+/-: zoom in/out

R: Ruler

P : pan

N: Notes

F: Fit selection

Middle mouse: pan

W: Workplane

Right mouse: Orbit

Commands

D: Drop to Workplane

Ctrl+D: Duplicate+repeat

Shift : select multiple

Ctrl+Z: Undo

Ctrl+C: Copy

Del: delete

Ctrl+V: Paste

Shortcuts

Functions

↑ ↓ →← : step move

Shift + Scale: Uniform scale

Ctrl + ↑ ↓ : Step move in Z

Alt + Scale: Scale center

Shift + ↑ ↓ : Step move

L: Align

Shift + rotate: 45° rotate

M: Mirror

Shape properties

Ctrl+G: Group

T: Transparent

Ctrl+Shift+G: ungroup

Ctrl+L: Lock/unlock

H: Hole

Ctrl+H: Hide

S: Solid

Ctrl+Shift+H: Show all

Resources

We're committed to providing everyone with access to our books. Visit <u>CADclass.org/pages/books</u> for a free or donation-based copy of this book and others.

CADclass.org/courses/Tinkercad

YouTube.com/c/HLModTech

YouTube.com/@AutodeskTinkercad

Youtube.com/@robmorrill1

Instructables.com/Tinkercad

ESA.int/Education/Moon_Camp/Tinkercad

Weareprintlab.com/projects/designing-for-3d-printing

<u>Contact Information:</u>

Ed@CADclass.org

(415) 941 - 4114

About CADclass

CADclass is a platform for students and instructors to learn CAD, 3D printing, Design, and Engineering. We write books, teach online classes, and curate a worldwide community of makers. We provide free and paid resources through our social channels, website, and partner network.

Our book Mastering Fusion 360 is available on Amazon or for a donation/free on our website - CADclass.org/pages/books

Online Courses:

Tinkercad in Twenty Days - Step-by-step Tinkercad projects for advancing your Tinkercad skills beyond this book! CADclass.org/courses/tinkercad

3D Printing Masterclass - Ender3 Assembly and use for beginners! CADclass.org/courses/3dp

Mastering Fusion 360 - 28 step-by-step projects in Autodesk Fusion. CADclass.org/courses/CAD

Cura Masterclass - Turn your 3D models into 3D printable designs with Cura by Ultimaker! CADclass.org/courses/cura

Advanced 3D Printer Maintenance and Calibration - Fine-tune your 3D printer to get perfect prints every time! CADclass.org/courses/calibrate

Socials:

Youtube.com/@CADclassOfficial | Tiktok.com/@cadclass
Twitter.com/cad_class |
Instagram.com/cadclassofficial

CERTIFICATE

OF COMPLETION

Send an email to
Ed@CADclass.org with
"Certificate" in the title to receive a
digital certificate of completion!

Ed Charlwood

What's Next?

Make things. Take things apart. Fiddle with mechanical objects. Fix a broken tool. Take a woodworking, glassblowing, ceramic, or welding class. Visit your local library and get to know your librarian. Study a topic that interests you. Talk to an expert. Oil squeaky doors. Try to recreate objects you see. Curate a list of YouTubers who do amazing things. Study the great inventors. Visit an art gallery or museum. Start a business. Go deeper into 3D printing and laser cutting. Share what you know with someone else. Solve a problem you have in your own life. Start small, dream big, and keep going. Do what you've always wanted to do.

Life is short; don't waste any time!

Cut Here

Made in the USA
Columbia, SC
24 July 2024

39258120R00063